SCUOLA D'INGLESE

1° livello

the adventures of
Pinocchio

⊙ GIUNTI Junior

Geppetto is
a poor carpenter and
he has no children.
One day he takes
a strange
piece of wood
and makes a puppet.

He makes
a head and
two eyes...

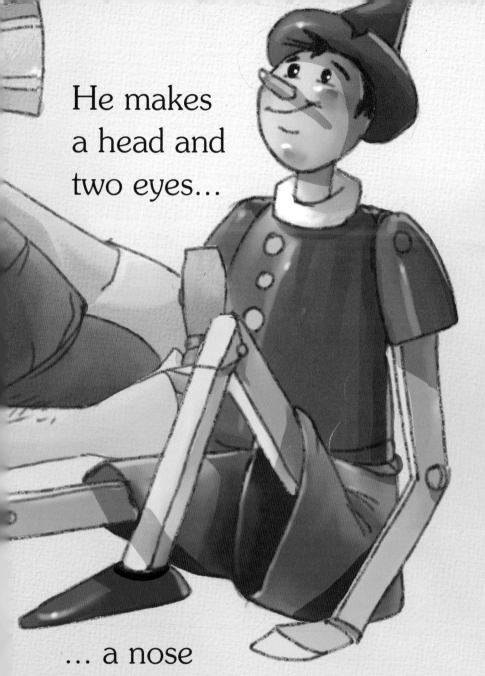

... a nose
and a mouth, two arms, two
hands, two legs and two feet.

3

Immediately the puppet
starts jumping around.
Geppetto is very happy.
The puppet is
his son now!

– You must go to school,
but first you need a name –
Geppetto says. – I can call
you Pinocchio.

Geppetto goes out
and sells his coat
to buy a spelling
book.

At home Pinocchio hears
a voice: – Hello, I'm
Jiminy Cricket. Be good
to Geppetto: he is
a good man!

Geppetto gives Pinocchio
the spelling book. – Go to
school and be a good boy!
Pinocchio leaves the house
with his spelling book
and...

... Jiminy Cricket follows him.

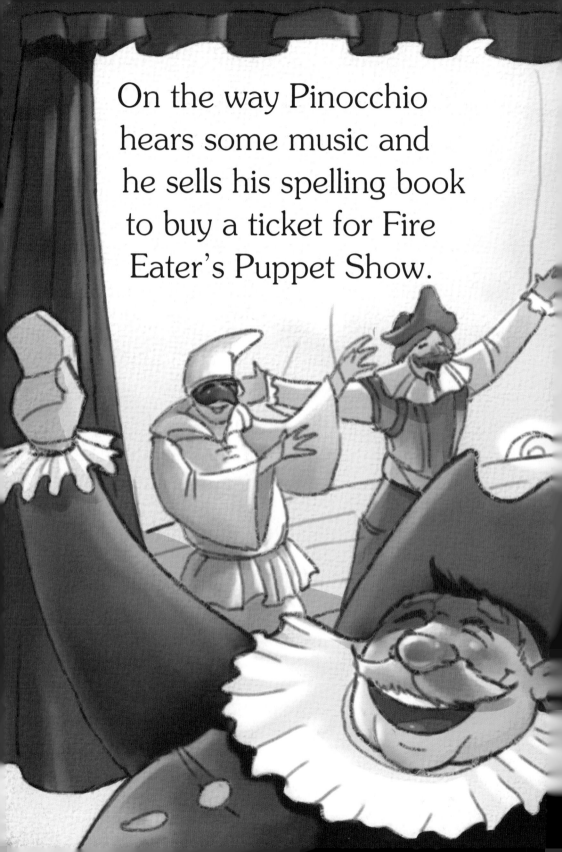

On the way Pinocchio hears some music and he sells his spelling book to buy a ticket for Fire Eater's Puppet Show.

Soon he is on stage singing and dancing with all the other puppets.

The show is a success
and Fire Eater wants
Pinocchio to stay.

– Remember that Geppetto wants you to go to school – says Jiminy Cricket.

Luckily Fire Eater knows
Geppetto and gives Pinocchio
five pieces of gold to take
to him.

– I want to buy Geppetto
a new coat with this
money! – says Pinocchio.

On the way home he meets
a cat and a fox and he tells
them about his good fortune.
– You can make more
money if you come
with us – says the cat.

– Where? – asks Pinocchio.
– To our magic field – the
fox says. – You bury the
money and you have
a tree of gold the next day.

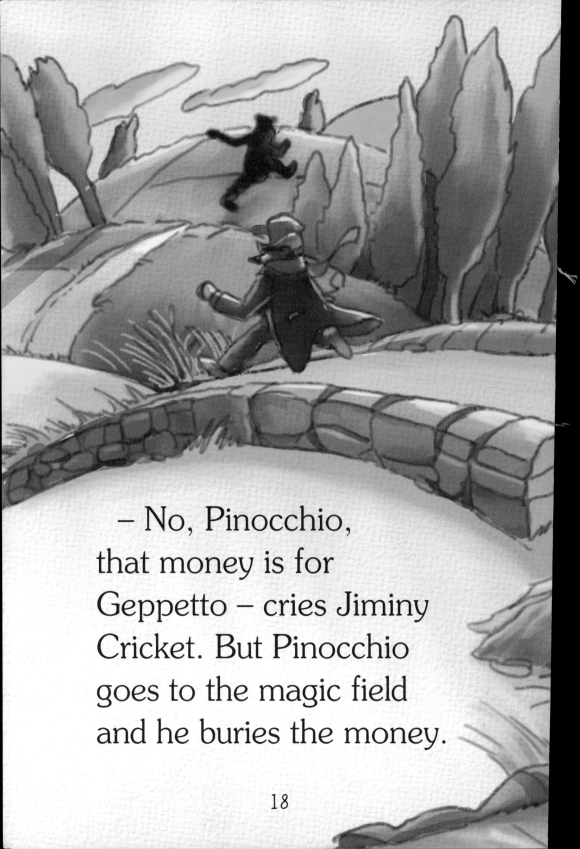

– No, Pinocchio,
that money is for
Geppetto – cries Jiminy
Cricket. But Pinocchio
goes to the magic field
and he buries the money.

The next day
he goes to the field
but there's no tree of
gold. There's only an
empty hole!

The money is not there!
He starts crying.

Near the field lives the
Blue Fairy. She hears
Pinocchio crying and she
goes to see what is wrong.

– There's a hole in my
pocket. The money
I want to take to
Geppetto is not here! –
cries Pinocchio.

But suddenly his nose
begins to grow.
– Are you sure? Don't lie.
Where is your money? –
the Blue Fairy asks.

– I don't know. It's not
in my pocket anymore! –
replies Pinocchio.
His nose goes on growing.

The Blue Fairy laughs: – When you tell a lie your nose grows! So Pinocchio promises not to tell any more lies.

– Go home and be
a good boy! – the
Blue Fairy says.
Pinocchio thanks the
Fairy and runs home.

But on the way he meets a boy. – Come to the Land of Toys with me! – he says. – Nobody goes to school there and you can play all day long!

– Don't listen to him –
says Jiminy Cricket.

– We can take the carriage
this evening – says
the boy.

Pinocchio forgets all the
promises to his father
and to the Fairy. They
jump up in the carriage
to the Land of Toys.

– Life is great here!
No books, no lessons and
we can play all the time! –
cries Pinocchio.

One day Pinocchio
notices he has
long, hairy ears...

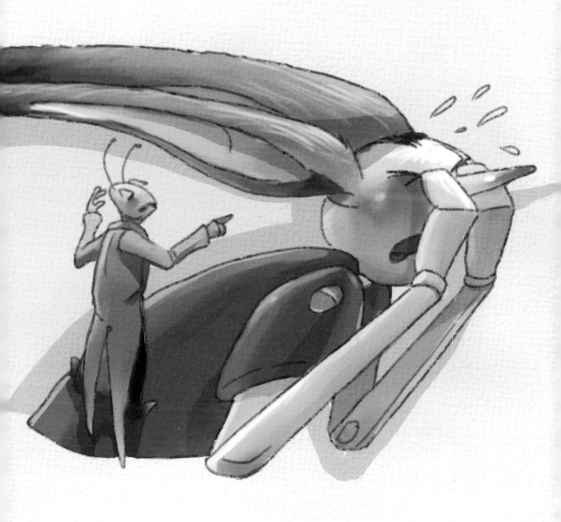

– You are turning into
a donkey! – says Jiminy
Cricket. – I want to go
home! – cries Pinocchio.

– Jump into the sea
and escape from here! –
says Jiminy Cricket.

So they jump into the
dark sea and swim in the
waves.

Then they see a light
in the dark.

They swim and swim right
into a whale's mouth.
– We are inside a whale! –
cries Jiminy Cricket.

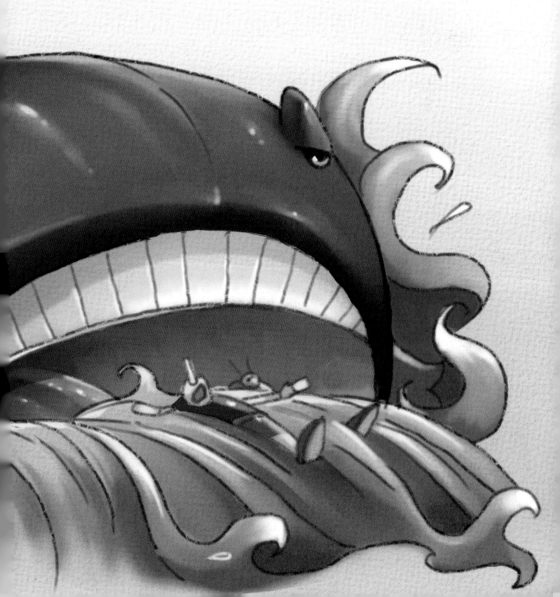

– Pinocchio! – a voice calls.
– What?! But it's you,
dad! – cries Pinocchio
so happy to see
Geppetto.

– We must get out of here and swim to land! – Pinocchio says.
When the whale opens its mouth they get out.

Pinocchio swims
and pulls Geppetto.
When they reach
dry land they are
very tired.

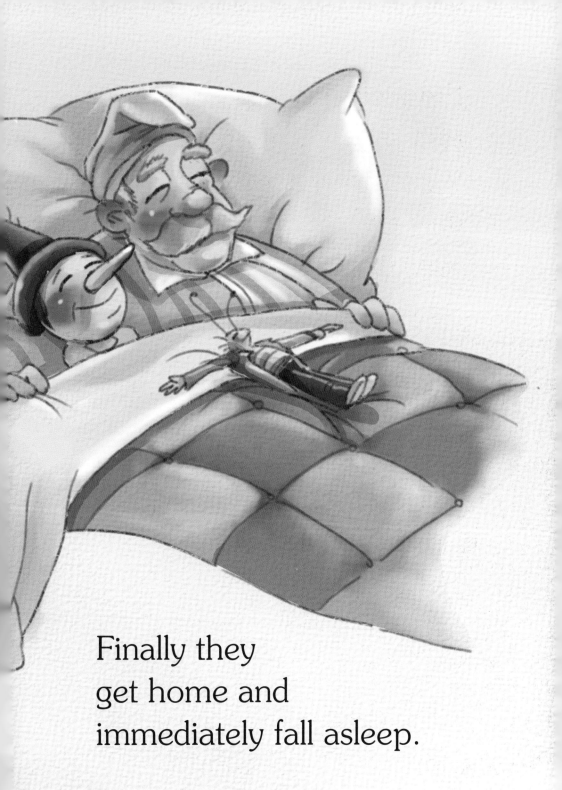

Finally they
get home and
immediately fall asleep.

The next day they
wake up and the Blue
Fairy is there.
– Look in the mirror! –
she says to Pinocchio.

Pinocchio is a real boy with blue eyes and brown hair.
– Oh, my son! – cries Geppetto with joy.

– You are a good boy:
this is your reward! –
says the Blue Fairy.

Pinocchio and Geppetto
are very happy and they
jump and laugh together!

TRADUZIONE
INGLESE / ITALIANO

Pinocchio

Pagina 2

Geppetto is a poor carpenter and he has no children.
One day he takes a strange piece of wood and makes a puppet.

Geppetto è un falegname povero e senza figli.
Un giorno prende uno strano pezzo di legno e costruisce un burattino.

Pagina 3

He makes a head and two eyes, a nose and a mouth, two arms, two hands, two legs and two feet.

Costruisce una testa e due occhi, un naso e una bocca, due braccia, due mani, due gambe e due piedi.

Pagina 4

Immediately the puppet starts jumping around.
Geppetto is very happy. The puppet is his son now!

Immediatamente il burattino comincia a saltare tutt'intorno.
Geppetto è molto felice. Il burattino è suo figlio ora!

Pagina 5

– You must go to school, but first you need a name – Geppetto says.

– I can call you Pinocchio.

– Devi andare a scuola, ma prima hai bisogno di un nome – dice Geppetto. – Ti posso chiamare Pinocchio.

Pagina 6
Geppetto goes out and sells his coat to buy a spelling book.

Geppetto esce e vende la sua giacca per comprare un abbecedario.

Pagina 7
At home Pinocchio hears a voice: – Hello, I'm Jiminy Cricket. Be good to Geppetto: he is a good man!

A casa Pinocchio sente una voce: – Ciao, sono il Grillo Parlante. Sii buono con Geppetto: è un brav'uomo!

Pagina 8
Geppetto gives Pinocchio the spelling book. – Go to school and be a good boy!
Pinocchio leaves the house with his spelling book and...

Geppetto dà a Pinocchio il suo abbecedario. – Vai a scuola e fai il bravo! Pinocchio esce di casa con l'abbecedario e...

Pagina 9
... Jiminy Cricket follows him.

... il Grillo Parlante lo segue.

Pagina 10
On the way Pinocchio hears some music and he sells his spelling book to buy a ticket for Fire Eater's Puppet Show.

Per la strada Pinocchio sente della musica e vende il suo abbecedario per comprare un biglietto per lo spettacolo di burattini di Mangiafuoco.

Pagina 11

Soon he is on stage singing and dancing with all the other puppets.

Presto è sul palco a cantare e a ballare con tutti gli altri burattini.

Pagina 12

The show is a success and Fire Eater wants Pinocchio to stay.

Lo spettacolo è un successo e Mangiafuoco vuole che Pinocchio resti.

Pagina 13

– Remember that Geppetto wants you to go to school – says Jiminy Cricket.

– Ricorda che Geppetto vuole che tu vada a scuola – dice il Grillo Parlante.

Pagina 14

Luckily Fire Eater knows Geppetto and gives Pinocchio five pieces of gold to take to him.

Per fortuna Mangiafuoco conosce Geppetto e dà a Pinocchio cinque monete d'oro da portargli.

Pagina 15

– I want to buy Geppetto a new coat with this money! – says Pinocchio.

– Voglio comprare a Geppetto una giacca nuova con questi soldi! – dice Pinocchio.

Pagina 16

On the way home he meets a cat and a fox and he tells them about his good fortune. – You can make more money if you come with us – says the cat.

Lungo la strada di casa incontra un gatto e una volpe e racconta loro della sua buona sorte. – Puoi fare più soldi se vieni con noi – dice il gatto.

Pagina 17

– Where? – asks Pinocchio. – To our magic field – the fox says. – You bury the money and you have a tree of gold the next day.

– Dove? – chiede Pinocchio. – Nel nostro campo magico – dice la volpe. – Si sotterra il denaro e il giorno dopo trovi un albero d'oro.

Pagina 18

– No, Pinocchio, that money is for Geppetto – cries Jiminy Cricket. But Pinocchio goes to the magic field and he buries the money.

– No, Pinocchio, quei soldi sono per Geppetto – grida il Grillo Parlante. Ma Pinocchio va al campo magico e sotterra il denaro.

Pagina 19

The next day he goes to the field but there's no tree of gold. There's only an empty hole!

Il giorno dopo ritorna al campo ma non c'è nessun albero d'oro. C'è solo una buca vuota!

Pagina 20

The money is not there! He starts crying.

Il denaro non c'è! Inizia a piangere.

Pagina 21

Near the field lives the Blue Fairy. She hears Pinocchio crying and she goes to see what is wrong.

Vicino al campo vive la Fata Turchina. Sente piangere Pinocchio e va a vedere cos'è che non va.

Pagina 22

– There's a hole in my pocket. The money I want to take to Geppetto is not here! – cries Pinocchio.

– C'è un buco nella mia tasca. I soldi che voglio portare a Geppetto non ci sono! – piange Pinocchio.

Pagina 23
But suddenly his nose begins to grow.
– Are you sure? Don't lie. Where is your money? – the Blue Fairy asks.

Ma improvvisamente il suo naso comincia a crescere.
– Sei sicuro? Non mentire. Dove sono i soldi? – chiede la Fata Turchina.

Pagina 24
– I don't know. It's not in my pocket anymore! – replies Pinocchio.
His nose goes on growing.

– Non lo so. Non sono più nella mia tasca! – replica Pinocchio.
Il suo naso continua a crescere.

Pagina 25
The Blue Fairy laughs: – When you tell a lie your nose grows!
So Pinocchio promises not to tell any more lies.

La Fata Turchina sorride: – Quando dici una bugia il tuo naso cresce!
Così Pinocchio promette di non raccontare più bugie.

Pagina 26
– Go home and be a good boy! – the Blue Fairy says.
Pinocchio thanks the Fairy and runs home.

– Vai a casa e sii buono! – dice la Fata Turchina.
Pinocchio ringrazia la Fata e corre a casa.

Pagina 27
But on the way he meets a boy. – Come to the Land of Toys with me!
– he says. – Nobody goes to school there and you can play all day long!

Ma lungo la strada incontra un ragazzo. – Vieni con me nel Paese dei Balocchi! – dice. – Nessuno va a scuola lì e si può giocare tutto il giorno!

Pagina 28

– Don't listen to him – says Jiminy Cricket.

– *Non ascoltarlo – dice il Grillo Parlante.*

Pagina 29

– We can take the carriage this evening – says the boy.

– *Possiamo prendere la carrozza questa sera – dice il ragazzo.*

Pagina 30

Pinocchio forgets all the promises to his father and to the Fairy.
They jump up in the carriage to the Land of Toys.

*Pinocchio dimentica tutte le promesse fatte a suo padre e alla Fata.
Saltano nella carrozza verso il Paese dei Balocchi.*

Pagina 31

– Life is great here! No books, no lessons and we can play all the time!
– cries Pinocchio.

– *La vita qui è meravigliosa! Niente libri, niente lezioni e possiamo
giocare tutto il tempo! – esclama Pinocchio.*

Pagina 32

One day Pinocchio notices he has long, hairy ears…

Un giorno Pinocchio si accorge di avere delle lunghe orecchie pelose…

Pagina 33

– You are turning into a donkey! – says Jiminy Cricket.
– I want to go home! – cries Pinocchio.

– *Ti stai trasformando in un asinello! – dice il Grillo Parlante.*
– *Voglio tornare a casa! – piange Pinocchio.*

Pagina 34

– Jump into the sea and escape from here! – says Jiminy Cricket.

– Buttati in mare e scappa di qui! – dice il Grillo Parlante.

Pagina 35

So they jump into the dark sea and swim in the waves.

Così si tuffano nel mare scuro e nuotano tra le onde.

Pagina 36

Then they see a light in the dark.

Poi vedono una luce nel buio.

Pagina 37

They swim and swim right into a whale's mouth.
– We are inside a whale! – cries Jiminy Cricket.

Nuotano e nuotano proprio dentro la bocca di una balena.
– Siamo dentro a una balena! – grida il Grillo Parlante.

Pagina 38

– Pinocchio! – a voice calls. – What?! But it's you, dad! – cries Pinocchio,
so happy to see Geppetto.

– Pinocchio! – una voce chiama. – Cosa?! Ma sei tu, babbo! – grida
Pinocchio così felice di vedere Geppetto.

Pagina 39

– We must get out of here and swim to land! – Pinocchio says.
When the whale opens its mouth they get out.

– Dobbiamo uscire da qui e nuotare verso terra! – dice Pinocchio.
Quando la balena apre la bocca escono fuori.

Pagina 40

Pinocchio swims and pulls Geppetto.
When they reach dry land they are very tired.

Pinocchio nuota e tira Geppetto.
Quando raggiungono la terraferma sono molto stanchi.

Pagina 41

Finally they get home and immediately fall asleep.

Alla fine arrivano a casa e si addormentano immediatamente.

Pagina 42

The next day they wake up and the Blue Fairy is there.
– Look in the mirror! – she says to Pinocchio.

Il mattino seguente si svegliano e la Fata Turchina è lì.
– Guardati allo specchio! – dice a Pinocchio.

Pagina 43

Pinocchio is a real boy with blue eyes and brown hair.
– Oh, my son! – cries Geppetto with joy.

Pinocchio è un bambino vero con gli occhi blu e i capelli marroni.
– Oh, figlio mio! – esclama Geppetto con gioia.

Pagina 44

– You are a good boy: this is your reward! – says the Blue Fairy.

– Sei un bravo bambino: questo è il tuo premio! – dice la Fata Turchina.

Pagina 45

Pinocchio and Geppetto are very happy and they jump and laugh together!

makes a out of a piece of . The puppet is alive and Geppetto gives him a spelling to go to . sells the spelling book to buy a for a puppet show. Fire Eater gives Pinocchio some to take to Geppetto. But Pinocchio tells a and a about his good fortune. They take

Pinocchio to a Magic and he buries the money. The next day the money is gone. The Blue arrives and Pinocchio lies to her, so his begins to grow very long. On the way home he meets a and he follows him to the Land of Toys. Here Pinocchio starts growing long like a . He runs away and jumps into the . He swims inside a and meets Geppetto. They arrive home and the Blue Fairy turns Pinocchio into a real .

Find the
Differences

Look carefully at the two pictures and find the 5 differences.

Osserva attentamente le due immagini e trova le 5 differenze.

A Wordsearch

Find 4 words of the story!

Trova 4 parole della storia!

FOX **CAT**

WHALE **PUPPET**

A	P	I	L	V	P
Y	F	O	X	C	U
U	B	N	A	K	P
H	T	J	C	D	P
S	W	H	A	L	E
Z	G	W	T	E	T
R	Q	O	X	F	M

What is this?

Join the numbers from one to eighteen!

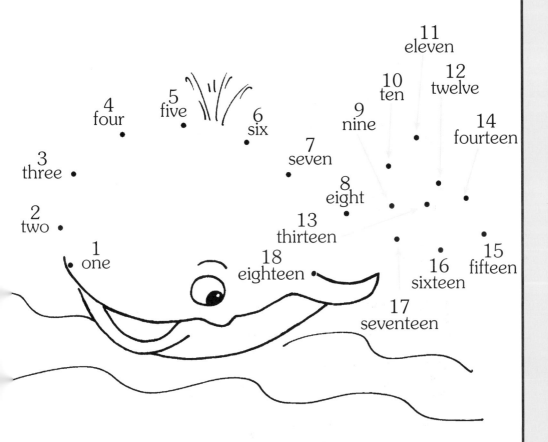

Unisci i numeri dall'uno al diciotto!

11 eleven
10 ten
12 twelve
9 nine
14 fourteen
4 four
5 five
6 six
7 seven
3 three
8 eight
2 two
13 thirteen
1 one
18 eighteen
15 fifteen
16 sixteen
17 seventeen

THIS IS A W _ _ _ _ _
IN THE SEA!

Match the Word with the picture!

BLUE FAIRY

PINOCCHIO

FIRE EATER

GEPPETTO

A Crossword

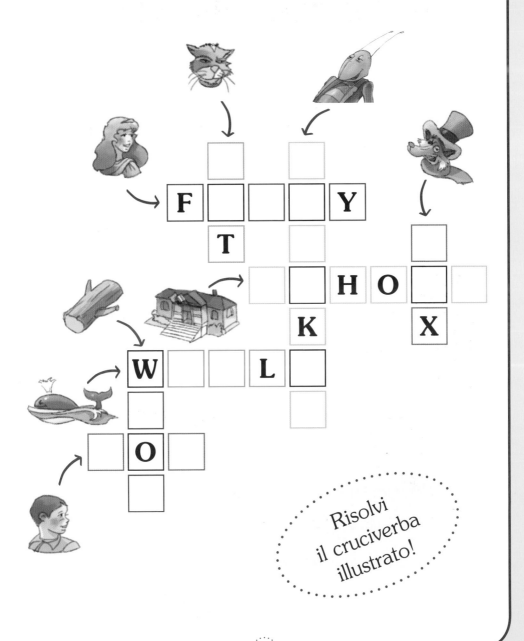

A Maze

Help Pinocchio to reach
the carriage to the Land of Toys!

Aiuta Pinocchio a raggiungere
la carrozza diretta al Paese dei Balocchi!

A little dictionary

BOY: RAGAZZO

CARPENTER: FALEGNAME

CAT: GATTO

COAT: GIACCA

CRICKET: GRILLO

DONKEY: ASINO

FAIRY: FATA

FIELD: CAMPO

FOX: VOLPE

LIE: BUGIA

MOUTH: BOCCA

NOSE: NASO

POCKET: TASCA

PUPPET: BURATTINO

SCHOOL: SCUOLA

SON: FIGLIO

WHALE: BALENA

WOOD: LEGNO

EMPTY: VUOTO • • • **aggettivi** • • •

GOOD: BUONO, BRAVO

HAIRY: PELOSO

HAPPY: FELICE

POOR: POVERO

TIRED: STANCO

to **BURY:** SOTTERRARE   • • • **verbi** • • •

to **BUY:** COMPRARE

to **ESCAPE:** SCAPPARE

to **FOLLOW:** SEGUIRE

to **GIVE:** DARE

to **JUMP:** SALTARE

to **GROW:** CRESCERE

to **LIE:** MENTIRE

to **MAKE:** FARE, COSTRUIRE

to **MEET:** INCONTRARE

to **PLAY:** GIOCARE

to **SELL:** VENDERE

to **SWIM:** NUOTARE

A cura di Gabriella Ballarin
Illustrazioni: Giulio Peranzoni
Progetto grafico: Romina Ferrari
Impaginazione: Simonetta Zuddas

Ristampa					Anno		
7	6	5	4	3	2016	2015	2014

www.giunti.it

© 2007, 2012 Giunti Editore S.p.A.
Via Bolognese, 165 - 50139 Firenze - Italia
Piazza Virgilio 4 - 20123 Milano - Italia

Prima edizione con CD: settembre 2012

Stampato presso Giunti Industrie Grafiche S.p.A.
Stabilimento di Prato